The Little Ants

Written by José-Luis Orozco
Illustrated by Rose Mary Berlin

Music for this selection and others by José-Luis Orozco is available from Arcoiris Records, P.O. Box 7428 Berkeley, CA 94707, USA and at www.joseluisorozco.com.

www. sra4kids.com

SRA/McGraw-Hill

A Division of The McGraw·Hill Companies

Send all inquiries to:
SRA/McGraw-Hill
8787 Orion Place
Columbus, OH 43240-4027

Printed in the United States of America.

ISBN 0-07-572414-6

3 4 5 6 7 8 9 QST 06 05 04 03

Over the little hills
and all the little roads,
the line of little ants
walks on and on.

The line of little ants,
the line of little ants,
the line of little ants
walks on and on.

Over the little hills
and all the little roads,
the line of little ants
walks on tippy-toes.

4

The line of little ants,
the line of little ants,
the line of little ants
walks on tippy-toes.

Over the little hills
and all the little roads,
the line of little ants
spins on and on.

The line of little ants,
the line of little ants,
the line of little ants
spins on and on.

Over the little hills
and all the little roads,
the line of little ants
jumps on and on.

8

The line of little ants,
the line of little ants,
the line of little ants
jumps on and on.

Over the little hills
and all the little roads,
the line of little ants
dances on and on.

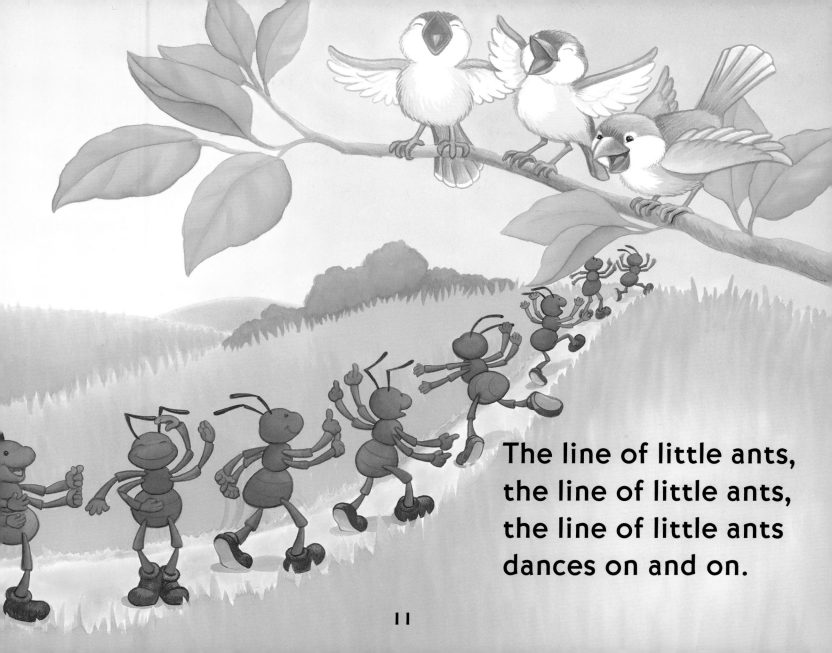

The line of little ants,
the line of little ants,
the line of little ants
dances on and on.

11

Over the little hills
and all the little roads,
the line of little ants
skates on and on.

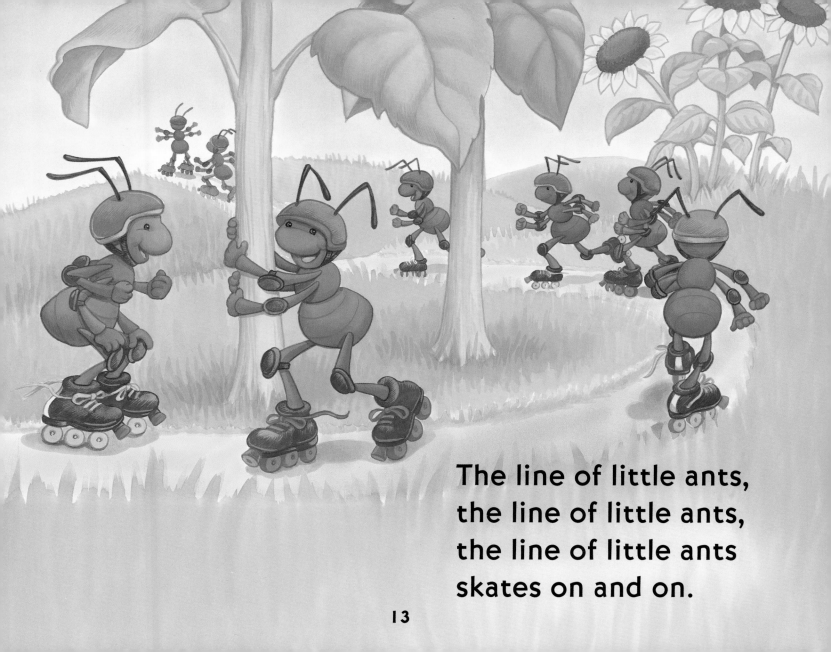

The line of little ants,
the line of little ants,
the line of little ants
skates on and on.

Over the little hills
and all the little roads,
the line of little ants
all waves good-bye.

The line of little ants,
the line of little ants,
the line of little ants
all waves good-bye.